Practice and homework

Year 3

This book is not photocopiable.

Rising Stars UK Ltd., 7 Hatchers Mews, Bermondsey Street,
London SE1 3GS

www.risingstars-uk.com

Every effort has been made to trace copyright holders and obtain their permission for the use of copyright materials. The author and publisher will gladly receive information enabling them to rectify any error or omission in subsequent editions.

All facts are correct at time of going to press.

First published as *New Framework Maths Practice and Homework Year 3*.
This reissue published 2011.
Text, design and layout © Rising Stars UK Ltd.

Cover design: Richard Scott
Design and illustration: Redmoor Design, Tavistock, Devon
Editorial consultant: Ann Todd

British Library Cataloguing in Publication Data
A CIP record for this book is available from the British Library.

ISBN: 978-1-84680-943-9

Printed by Craft Print International Ltd., Singapore

Contents

Coverage of Primary Framework for mathematics 4

How to use this book 6

Counting in steps of 10 and 100 8

Counting in 3s, 4s and 5s 9

Many multiples 10

Making and ordering numbers 11

Estimating 12

Rounding numbers to nearest 100 14

Fractions of shapes 15

Equivalent fractions 16

Fractions of a set 17

Mixed numbers 18

Using mathematical vocabulary 19

Adding and subtracting 9 or 11 20

Addition by partitioning 21

Drawing number lines for addition problems 22

Drawing number lines for subtraction problems 23

Finding the difference between two numbers 24

Missing numbers 25

Understanding multiplication 26

Multiplication facts 27

Division by grouping 28

Division by sharing 29

Division facts 30

Division with remainders 31

Rounding up or down 32

Multiplying and dividing by 10 34

Putting it into practice 35

Word problems 36

Number puzzles 38

Finding totals 39

Money problems 40

Calculating change 42

Measuring length 43

Length problems 44

Mass problems 45

Measuring mass 46

Measuring capacity 48

Capacity problems 50

Choosing units 51

Negative numbers (temperature) 52

Units of time 53

Reading times 54

Time problems 55

2D shapes 56

3D shapes 57

Lines of symmetry 58

Position and direction 59

Right angles 60

Sorting information 61

Drawing bar charts 62

Pictograms 64

Coverage of Primary Framework for mathematics

	Page number
Using and applying mathematics	
Solve one-step and two-step problems involving numbers, money or measures, including time, choosing and carrying out appropriate calculations	19, 32, 33, 35, 36, 37, 39, 40, 41, 42, 50, 51
Represent the information in a puzzle or problem using numbers, images or diagrams; use these to find a solution and present it in context, where appropriate using £.p notation or units of measure	11, 22, 23, 36, 37
Follow a line of enquiry by deciding what information is important; make and use lists, tables and graphs to organise and interpret the information	35, 36, 37
Identify patterns and relationships involving numbers or shapes, and use these to solve problems	20
Describe and explain methods, choices and solutions to puzzles and problems, orally and in writing, using pictures and diagrams	32, 33
Counting and understanding number	
Read, write and order whole numbers to at least 1000 and position them on a number line; count on from and back to zero in single-digit steps or multiples of 10	8, 12, 13
Partition three-digit numbers into multiples of 100, 10 or 1 in different ways	21
Round two-digit or three-digit numbers to the nearest 10 or 100 and give estimates for their sums and differences	14
Read and write proper fractions (e.g. $\frac{3}{7}$, $\frac{9}{10}$) interpreting the denominator as the parts of a whole and the numerator as the number of parts; identify and estimate fractions of shapes; use diagrams to compare fractions and establish equivalents	15, 16
Knowing and using number facts	
Derive and recall all addition and subtraction facts for each number to 20, sums and differences of multiples of 10 and number pairs that total 100	38
Derive and recall multiplication facts for the 2, 3, 4, 5, 6 and 10 times-tables and the corresponding division facts; recognise multiples of 2, 5 or 10 up to 1000	9, 10, 27, 29, 35
Use knowledge of number operations and corresponding inverses, including doubling and halving, to estimate and check calculations	20, 26, 29, 35
Calculating	
Add or subtract mentally combinations of one-digit and two-digit numbers	25
Develop and use written methods to record, support or explain addition and subtraction of two-digit and three-digit numbers	21, 22, 23, 24, 25
Multiply one-digit and two-digit numbers by 10 or 100, and describe the effect	34, 35

	Page number
Use practical and informal written methods to multiply and divide two-digit numbers (e.g. 13 × 3, 50 ÷ 4); round remainders up or down, depending on the context	26, 27, 28, 31, 32, 33
Understand that division is the inverse of multiplication and vice versa and use to derive and record related multiplication and division number sentences	27, 29
Find unit fractions of numbers and quantities (e.g. ½, ⅓, ¼ and ⅛ of 12 litres)	17
Understanding shape	
Relate 2D shapes and 3D solids to drawings of them; describe, visualise, classify, draw and make the shapes	56, 57
Draw and complete shapes with reflective symmetry; draw the reflection of a shape in a mirror line along one side	58
Read and record the vocabulary of position, direction and movement, using the four compass directions to describe movement about a grid	59
Use a set-square to draw right angles and to identify right angles in 2D shapes; compare angles with a right angle; recognise that a straight line is equivalent to two right angles	60
Measuring	
Know the relationships between kilometres and metres, metres and centimetres, kilograms and grams, litres and millilitres; choose and use appropriate units to estimate, measure and record measurements	44, 45, 48, 49, 50, 51
Read, to the nearest division and half-division, scales that are numbered or partially numbered; use the information to measure and draw to a suitable degree of accuracy	43, 46, 47, 48, 49, 52
Read the time on a 12-hour digital clock and to the nearest five minutes on an analogue clock; calculate time intervals and find start or end times for a given time interval	54, 55
Handling data	
Answer a question by collecting, organising and interpreting data; use tally charts, frequency tables, pictograms and bar charts to represent results and illustrate observations; use ICT to create a simple bar chart	61, 62, 63, 64
Use Venn diagrams or Carroll diagrams to sort data and objects using more than one criterion	61

How to use this book

New Medal Maths has been created to provide you with lots of practice to support your maths learning.

To make it more fun for you, the activities are organised around an Olympic Games theme including sporting topics, training tips and the bronze, silver and gold medals. The medals indicate three different levels of difficulty.

As Pierre de Coubertin, the founder of the Modern Olympic Games, said "The most important thing in the Olympic Games is not to win but to take part …"!

Practice and more practice is the best method for getting results and improving your performance in maths.

For the best results:

a) read the explanation;

b) complete the questions at the most appropriate level;

c) use the hints and tips to help you;

d) see if you can complete the next level of questions!

Explanations
Explanations and examples are given to support you working independently.

Bronze Medal Questions
These questions are an ideal starting point. They support the work covered in the Silver questions.

Silver Medal Questions
These questions are set at the expected level for Year 3 as presented by the Primary Framework.

> **Primary Framework for mathematics**
> Every objective is covered through an explanation, three levels of questions and hints and tips.

NUMBER AND ALGEBRA

Understanding multiplication

Sports Shop Price List

T-shirts	£4	Sweatshirts	£8	Cap	£3
Tracksuit	£10	Football	£3	Bat	£7
Gloves	£6	Badge	£1	Socks	£2

> **Gold Medal Questions**
> These questions are a bit harder. They extend the work of the Silver questions.

 Bronze

Work out how much it would cost to buy these items from the sports shop.
Write each one as a multiplication sum.

For example, 5 footballs is $5 \times £3 = £15$

1. 4 pairs of socks
2. 3 caps
3. 2 tracksuits

Work out how many of the following you could buy with £20.

4. tracksuits
5. badges
6. footballs

 Silver

Work out how much it would cost to buy these items from the sports shop.
Write each one as a multiplication sum.

For example, 5 footballs is $5 \times £3 = £15$

1. 4 T-shirts
2. 8 footballs
3. 10 pairs of socks

Work out how many of the following you could buy with £20.

4. T-shirts
5. footballs
6. sweatshirts

 **Gold**

Work out how much it would cost to buy these items from the sports shop.
Write each one as a multiplication sum.

For example, 5 footballs is $5 \times £3 = £15$

1. 6 pairs of gloves
2. 13 tracksuits
3. 20 pairs of socks

Work out how many of the following you could buy with £20.

4. caps and socks
5. footballs and bats
6. badges and gloves

> **Questions**
> There are hundreds of questions covering all the content for the Primary Framework.

Training Tips
- Multiplication is the same as repeated addition.
  So $5 \times 3 = 3 + 3 + 3 + 3 + 3 = 15$

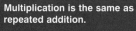 

26

> **Hints and Tips**
> Hints and tips to help you answer the questions.

> **Themes**
> Everyday situations, and a focus on sport, are used within the questions to put the maths into context.

Counting in steps of 10 and 100

Look at these sequences of numbers:

126, 136, 146, 156, 166   256, 356, 456, 556, 656

Which numbers would come next in each sequence? | 176 | | 756 |

 Bronze

Write the next five numbers in these sequences.

1. 30, 40, 50…
2. 100, 90…
3. 56, 66, 76…
4. 43, 53, 63…
5. 98, 88, 78…
6. 100, 200, 300…
7. 800, 700, 600…
8. 700, 600, 500…
9. 400, 500, 600…
10. 350, 450, 550…

 Silver

Write the next five numbers in these sequences.

1. 70, 80, 90…
2. 130, 120, 110…
3. 89, 99, 109…
4. 134, 144, 154…
5. 86, 96, 106…
6. 250, 350, 450…
7. 980, 880, 780…
8. 835, 735, 635…
9. 313, 413, 513…
10. 931, 831, 731…

 Gold

Write the next five numbers in these sequences.

1. 743, 753, 763…
2. 328, 318, 308…
3. 974, 964, 954…
4. 469, 479, 489…
5. 935, 925, 915…
6. 653, 753…
7. 944, 844…
8. 906, 806…
9. 1133, 1033…
10. 1265, 1165…

 **Training Tips**

- When counting in tens, the digit in the units column does not change.
- When counting in steps of 100 the tens and units do not change.

Counting in 3s, 4s and 5s

> 2, 7, 12, 17…

This pattern goes forward in steps of 5.

The next numbers would be 22, 27, 32, 37, 42…

Bronze

Write the rule to describe the sequence and write the next five numbers.

1. 0, 3, 6, 9…

2. 5, 10, 15, 20…

3. 16, 14, 12, 10…

4. 4, 8, 12, 16…

5. 75, 70, 65, 60…

6. 29, 27, 25, 23…

7. 12, 16, 20, 24…

8. 2, 5, 8, 11…

Silver

Write the rule to describe the sequence and write the next five numbers.

1. 38, 34, 30, 26…

2. 11, 16, 21, 26…

3. 77, 74, 71, 68…

4. 1, 4, 7, 10…

5. 94, 89, 84, 79…

6. 40, 36, 32, 28…

7. 3, 8, 13, 18…

8. 66, 69, 72, 75…

Gold

Write the rule to describe the sequence and write the next five numbers.

There are some missing numbers to fill in here too.

1. 84, 88, 92…

2. 13, 16, ☐ , 22…

3. 117, 113, 109…

4. 83, ☐ , 93, 98…

5. 97, ☐ , 87, 82…

6. 85, 88, ☐ , 94…

7. 64, 68, 72…

8. ☐ , 52, 49, 46…

Training Tips

- Look for a pattern in the units.
- Always look at the first two numbers first.

Many multiples

'Multiples' means the same as 'lots of' or 'counting in steps of'.

A multiple of 2 could be 2, 4, 6, 8…   A multiple of 5 could be 5, 10, 15, 20…

Some numbers are multiples of many other numbers. 10 is a multiple of 2, 5 and 10!

Bronze

Use a 100 square. Colour red all the multiples of 2. Colour blue all the multiples of 5. Colour green all the multiples of 10.

1. Which numbers are a multiple of 10?

2. Which numbers are a multiple of 2 and 5?

3. Which numbers are a multiple of 5 only?

4. Which numbers are a multiple of 2, 5 and 10?

5. Look at the multiples of 10. What do you notice about them?

Silver

5	15	22	28	30
35	36	40	45	50
52	55	56	60	65
74	80	88	95	100

Look at the numbers above.

1. Which are multiples of 5?

2. Write three multiples of 2.

3. Which are multiples of 10 greater than 36?

4. Which are multiples of 5 less than 56?

5. Which is a multiple of 2 and 10?

Gold

Use a number line to 30. See if you can find:

1. The multiples of 2, 5 and 10

2. A multiple of 2 and 5 that is greater than 10

3. Two multiples of 3 and 2 that are less than 15

4. The multiples of 5 but not 10

5. A multiple of 4 and 5

6. A multiple of 3 and 5 that comes between 10 and 20

Training Tips

- Multiples of 2 end in 0, 2, 4, 6 or 8.
- Multiples of 5 end in 0 or 5.
- Multiples of 10 end in 0.

Making and ordering numbers

When the digits 5, 2 and 7 are inputted into a 'Randomiser' machine, the possible numbers generated are:

527   572   752   725   257   275

When written in order, these become:

257   275   527   572   725   752

Bronze

Work out all the possible numbers when these digits are put into the machine, write them in order from lowest to highest and explain how you did it.

1. ⬚2⬚ ⬚5⬚ ⬚3⬚

2. ⬚6⬚ ⬚1⬚ ⬚9⬚

3. ⬚1⬚ ⬚6⬚ ⬚8⬚

4. ⬚3⬚ ⬚7⬚ ⬚1⬚

5. ⬚8⬚ ⬚2⬚ ⬚6⬚

Silver

Work out all the possible numbers when these digits are put into the machine, write them in order from lowest to highest and explain how you did it.

1. ⬚4⬚ ⬚5⬚ ⬚6⬚

2. ⬚1⬚ ⬚1⬚ ⬚9⬚

3. ⬚0⬚ ⬚5⬚ ⬚3⬚

4. ⬚7⬚ ⬚4⬚ ⬚6⬚ ⬚2⬚

5. ⬚1⬚ ⬚0⬚ ⬚6⬚ ⬚7⬚

Gold

Work out all the possible numbers when these digits are put into the machine, write them in order from lowest to highest and explain how you did it.

1. ⬚1⬚ ⬚0⬚ ⬚3⬚ ⬚2⬚

2. ⬚8⬚ ⬚7⬚ ⬚6⬚ ⬚8⬚

3. ⬚9⬚ ⬚9⬚ ⬚4⬚ ⬚8⬚

4. ⬚3⬚ ⬚0⬚ ⬚6⬚ ⬚9⬚

5. ⬚5⬚ ⬚5⬚ ⬚7⬚ ⬚5⬚

Training Tips

● When writing numbers in order, look at the hundreds then the tens then the units.

Estimating

In the javelin throw, the judges have to estimate how far each contestant has thrown their javelin.

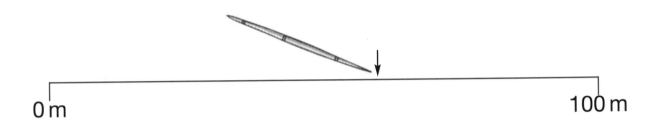

0 m   100 m

This contestant has thrown his javelin approximately 60 m.

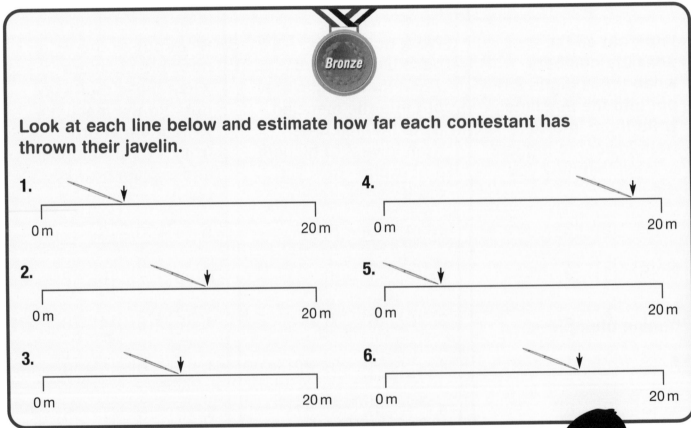

Look at each line below and estimate how far each contestant has thrown their javelin.

1.

0 m   20 m

2.

0 m   20 m

3.

0 m   20 m

4.

0 m   20 m

5.

0 m   20 m

6.

0 m   20 m

Training Tips

● Make sure you check the length of the number line (look at the end point).

● Work out what number would be halfway and decide if the javelin has gone more than or less than halfway.

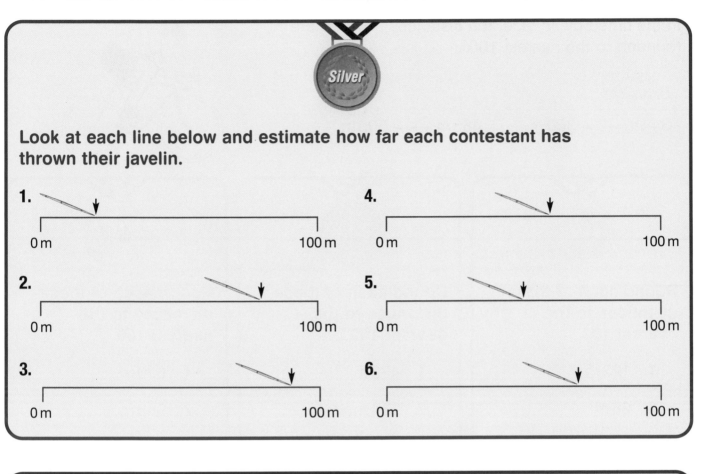

Look at each line below and estimate how far each contestant has thrown their javelin.

1.

0 m   100 m

2.

0 m   100 m

3.

0 m   100 m

4.

0 m   100 m

5.

0 m   100 m

6.

0 m   100 m

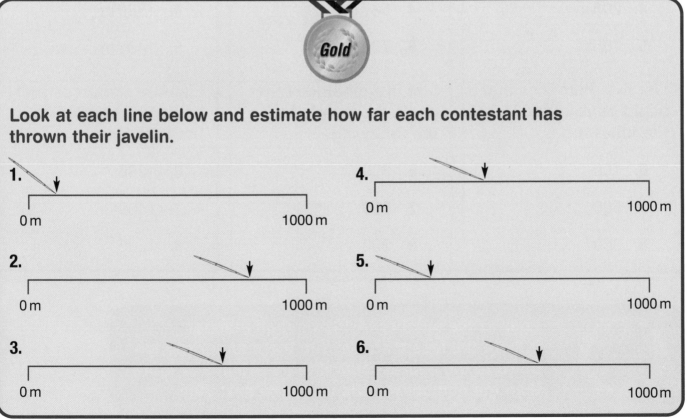

Look at each line below and estimate how far each contestant has thrown their javelin.

1.

0 m   1000 m

2.

0 m   1000 m

3.

0 m   1000 m

4.

0 m   1000 m

5.

0 m   1000 m

6.

0 m   1000 m

Rounding numbers to nearest 100

In the timed cycle race, the distances covered are rounded to the nearest 100.

Example

347 m ⟶ 300 m   486 m ⟶ 500 m

Bronze

Round each of these distances to the nearest 100.

1. 123 m
2. 98 m
3. 146 m
4. 203 m
5. 165 m

List five distances that could be rounded to the following:

6. 100
7. 500
8. 300

Silver

Round each of these distances to the nearest 100.

1. 433 m
2. 124 m
3. 350 m
4. 587 m
5. 730 m

List five distances that could be rounded to the following:

6. 800
7. 500
8. 300

Gold

Round each of these distances to the nearest 100.

1. 650 m
2. 985 m
3. 261 m
4. 1369 m
5. 1431 m

List five distances that could be rounded to the following:

6. 1200
7. 1400
8. 1600

Training Tips

● **Look at the number of 10s in each number. If there are less than five 10s the number rounds down to the nearest 100. If there are five or more then the number rounds up to the next 100.**

Fractions of shapes

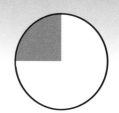

$\frac{1}{4}$ of this circle has been shaded blue leaving $\frac{3}{4}$ unshaded.

Bronze

1. Draw a rectangle with $\frac{1}{4}$ green.

2. Draw a triangle with $\frac{1}{2}$ red.

3. What fraction of this shape is shaded?

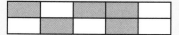

4. Take 20 cubes and make a shape which is $\frac{1}{2}$ red and $\frac{1}{4}$ blue. What fraction is not red or blue?

5. This is half a shape.

Can you draw the whole shape?

Silver

1. Draw an equilateral triangle that is $\frac{1}{2}$ red.

2. Draw a square with $\frac{1}{3}$ orange.

3. What fraction of this shape is shaded?

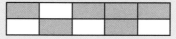

4. Take 16 cubes and make a shape that is $\frac{1}{8}$ yellow, $\frac{1}{4}$ green and $\frac{1}{8}$ red. What fraction is not yellow, green or red?

5. This is half a shape.

Can you draw the whole shape?

Gold

1. Draw a rectangle with $\frac{1}{10}$ purple and $\frac{1}{2}$ pink.

2. What fraction of this shape is shaded?

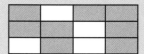

Can you write this fraction another way?

3. Take 24 cubes and make a shape that is $\frac{3}{8}$ red, $\frac{1}{8}$ black and $\frac{1}{4}$ white. What fraction is not red, black or white?

4. This is a quarter of a shape.

Can you draw the whole shape?

Training Tips

- When dividing your shape, make sure that all the parts are the same size.

- When reading fractions, make sure you read the top number first.

Equivalent fractions

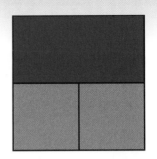

'Equivalent fractions' means two fractions that are the same.

For example $\frac{1}{2}$ is the same as $\frac{2}{4}$.

Bronze

For each of these, draw a square and colour in the fraction shown. Which ones are equivalent fractions?

1. $\frac{1}{2}$

2. $\frac{1}{8}$

3. $\frac{2}{4}$

4. $\frac{4}{8}$

5. $\frac{1}{4}$

6. $\frac{4}{4}$

7. $\frac{2}{8}$

8. $\frac{2}{2}$

9. $\frac{3}{4}$

10. $\frac{6}{8}$

Silver

For each of these, draw a square and colour in the fraction shown. Which ones are equivalent fractions?

1. $\frac{4}{8}$

2. $\frac{3}{4}$

3. $\frac{1}{2}$

4. $\frac{2}{2}$

5. $\frac{1}{4}$

6. $\frac{6}{8}$

7. $\frac{5}{10}$

8. $\frac{2}{4}$

9. $\frac{8}{8}$

10. $\frac{2}{8}$

Gold

For each of these, draw a square and colour in the fraction shown. Which ones are equivalent fractions?

1. $\frac{5}{10}$

2. $\frac{3}{4}$

3. $\frac{3}{6}$

4. $\frac{1}{2}$

5. $\frac{6}{8}$

6. $\frac{2}{2}$

7. $\frac{1}{4}$

8. $\frac{2}{6}$

9. $\frac{8}{8}$

10. $\frac{1}{3}$

Training Tips

● The bottom number of the fraction tells you how many parts the shape must be divided into. The top number of the fraction tells you how many parts to colour in.

Fractions of a set

A set of objects can also be divided into fractions.

For example $\frac{1}{2}$ of this set of 10 balls is blue.

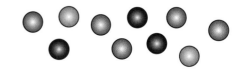

Bronze

Draw pictures to show the following:

1. 10 cars, one half blue

2. 12 biscuits, $\frac{1}{4}$ chocolate

3. 8 pencils, $\frac{1}{2}$ red

4. 8 children, one quarter girls

5. 16 lorries, one half brown

6. 14 balls, one half green

7. 4 apples, $\frac{1}{4}$ green

8. 12 buttons, $\frac{1}{2}$ black

Silver

Draw pictures to show the following:

1. 10 cars, $\frac{1}{10}$ blue

2. 12 biscuits, $\frac{1}{3}$ chocolate

3. 16 children, $\frac{1}{4}$ girls

4. 20 flowers, one fifth pink

5. 20 triangles, one tenth orange

6. 30 balls, one half green

7. 15 apples, one third green

8. 10 buttons, $\frac{1}{5}$ brown and $\frac{1}{2}$ black

Gold

Draw pictures to show the following:

1. 20 cars, one half blue and one quarter red

2. 28 pencils, $\frac{1}{4}$ red and $\frac{1}{2}$ green

3. 20 people, $\frac{1}{5}$ children and $\frac{1}{4}$ women

4. 15 lorries, $\frac{1}{5}$ brown and $\frac{1}{3}$ black

5. 10 triangles, one half yellow and one fifth orange

6. 24 balls, $\frac{1}{3}$ red and $\frac{1}{4}$ green

7. 24 apples, one sixth green

8. 12 buttons, $\frac{1}{3}$ brown and $\frac{1}{4}$ blue

Training Tips

● When dividing a set of objects into parts to find a fraction, make sure each part has the same number of objects in it.

Mixed numbers

A mixed number is made from a whole number and a fraction.

$2\frac{1}{2}$ is a mixed number. It is shown like this on a number line:

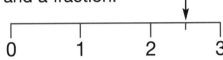

Bronze

For each number line write what mixed number is shown.

1.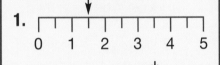

2.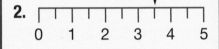

3.

Draw number lines between the numbers given. Then show the fractions on the number line.

4. 3 to 5. Show $3\frac{1}{2}$ and $4\frac{1}{2}$

5. 7 to 9. Show $7\frac{1}{2}$ and $8\frac{1}{2}$

6. 4 to 7. Show $4\frac{1}{2}$, $5\frac{1}{2}$ and $6\frac{1}{2}$

Silver

For each number line write what mixed number is shown.

1.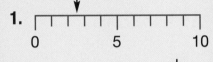

2.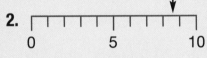

3.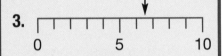

Draw number lines between the numbers given. Then show the fractions on the number line.

4. 0 to 3. Show $1\frac{1}{4}$, $1\frac{1}{2}$ and $2\frac{1}{4}$

5. 2 to 5. Show $2\frac{1}{2}$, $3\frac{1}{4}$ and $4\frac{1}{4}$

6. 3 to 6. Show $3\frac{1}{2}$, $4\frac{1}{4}$ and $5\frac{1}{2}$

Gold

For each number line write what mixed number is shown.

1.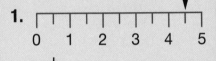

2.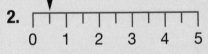

3.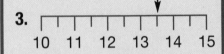

Draw number lines between the numbers given. Then show the fractions on the number line.

4. 0 to 3. Show $\frac{1}{4}$, $1\frac{1}{2}$ and $2\frac{1}{4}$

5. 4 to 7. Show $4\frac{1}{2}$, $5\frac{1}{4}$ and $6\frac{3}{4}$

6. 6 to 9. Show $6\frac{1}{4}$, $6\frac{3}{4}$, $7\frac{1}{2}$ and $7\frac{3}{4}$

Training Tips

● To read the position on the number line, look at the whole numbers first.

Using mathematical vocabulary

Bronze

1. 27 add 10 makes ☐
2. 4 plus 18 makes ☐
3. The difference between 17 and 6 is ☐
4. Which two numbers could have a sum of 20?
5. What must I add to 14 to make 19?
6. How many are 10 and 3 altogether?
7. 17 minus 11 leaves ☐
8. Add 12 to 6.
9. How many more is 10 than 4?
10. The total of 16 and 5 is ☐

Silver

1. 60 plus 40 is ☐
2. What is the total of 18 and 27?
3. What must I add to 19 to make 30?
4. The difference between 18 and 3 is ☐
5. How many are 12 and 37 altogether?
6. How many more is 25 than 16?
7. 23 minus 10 leaves ☐
8. 30 subtract 15 is ☐
9. How many less is 14 than 22?
10. The total of 12 and 13 is ☐

Gold

1. The difference between 75 and 30 is ☐
2. How many are 21 and 35 altogether?
3. The sum of 17 and 23 is ☐
4. 46 minus 15 leaves ☐
5. What must I add to 40 to make 97?
6. How many less is 17 than 50?
7. Which two numbers have a sum of 37?
8. How many more is 56 than 21?
9. What is the total of 45 and 31?
10. Add 60 to 14.

Training Tips

- Subtraction is the opposite of addition so use this to check your answers.

Adding and subtracting 9 or 11

Adding 9 or 11 to a number is easy if you add 10 first.
Remember $11 = 10 + 1$ and $9 = 10 - 1$

$$58 + 9 = 58 + 10 - 1 = 68 - 1 = 67$$

$$74 + 11 = 74 + 10 + 1 = 84 + 1 = 85$$

The same rule applies for adding 19, 29, 39…
21, 31, 41…

The same rule applies when **subtracting** 9 or 11.
But when you **subtract** 11 remember to -10 then -1
and when you subtract 9, -10 but then $+1$ back on.

$$73 - 11 = 73 - 10 - 1 = 63 - 1 = 62$$

$$61 - 9 = 61 - 10 + 1 = 51 + 1 = 52$$

Training Tips

- If you are adding 9, take away 1 from the 10.

- If you are adding 11, add 1 to the 10.

- If you are subtracting 9, add 1 to the 10.

- If you are subtracting 11, take away 1 from the 10.

Bronze

Try these sums:

1. $38 + 11 =$

2. $44 + 9 =$

3. $27 + 21 =$

4. $24 + 19 =$

5. $37 - 9 =$

6. $40 - 9 =$

7. $48 - 11 =$

8. $32 - 19 =$

Silver

Try these sums:

1. $46 + 29 =$

2. $63 + 31 =$

3. $29 + 59 =$

4. $69 + 39 =$

5. $47 - 41 =$

6. $98 - 79 =$

7. $241 - 9 =$

8. $145 - 31 =$

Gold

Try these sums:

1. $631 + 51 =$

2. $258 + 79 =$

3. $647 + 89 =$

4. $369 + 91 =$

5. $236 - 59 =$

6. $148 - 99 =$

7. $263 - 41 =$

8. $411 - 51 =$

Addition by partitioning

When adding two-digit numbers together, sometimes it is easier to break them down into their hundreds, tens and units.

Example

$$61 + 38 = 60 + 1 + 30 + 8$$
$$= 90 + 9$$
$$= 99$$

$$256 + 133 = 200 + 50 + 6 + 100 + 30 + 3$$
$$= 300 + 80 + 9$$
$$= 389$$

Bronze

Choose two numbers from below and add them together.
Which numbers do you need to use to make the biggest total?
What about the smallest total?

31	16	24	30
52	45	11	32
25	41	33	14
22	43	15	

Silver

Choose two numbers from below and add them together.
Which numbers do you need to use to make the biggest total?
What about the smallest total?

71	56	108	49
224	92	364	88
390	57	125	65
47	69	84	167

Gold

Choose two numbers from below and add them together.
Which numbers do you need to use to make the biggest total?
What about the smallest total?

256	479	539
219	364	506
424	169	373
106	453	347

Training Tips

● **Make sure you add hundreds to hundreds and tens to tens.**

Drawing number lines for addition problems

Number lines are a great tool for working out difficult addition sums.

Let's try 87 + 46 =

46 is made up of 4 tens and 6 units so that is what must be added onto 87.

So 87 + 46 = 133

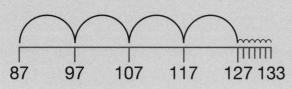

87   97   107   117   127 133

The same can be done for three-digit numbers.

254 + 431 =

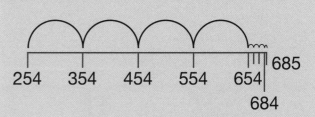

254   354   454   554   654| 685

684

Bronze

Draw number lines to help you work out the following:

1. 40 + 35 =
2. 46 + 22 =
3. 38 + 31 =
4. 54 + 34 =
5. 29 + 41 =
6. 61 + 33 =
7. 74 + 25 =

Silver

Draw number lines to help you work out the following:

1. 53 + 39 =
2. 86 + 42 =
3. 76 + 32 =
4. 84 + 53 =
5. 92 + 87 =
6. 106 + 57 =
7. 124 + 63 =

Gold

Draw number lines to help you work out the following:

1. 369 + 124 =
2. 401 + 258 =
3. 307 + 234 =
4. 428 + 115 =
5. 117 + 209 =
6. 356 + 487 =
7. 294 + 631 =

Training Tips

- Start with the biggest number and add on the smallest number.
- Add on the hundreds first, then the tens then the units.

Drawing number lines for subtraction problems

Number lines are also a useful tool for working out subtraction problems. They are drawn exactly the same as for addition. But remember – if you are subtracting a number you must go backwards along the number line.

Example

86 − 41 =

41 is 4 tens and 1 unit so that must be taken away from 86.

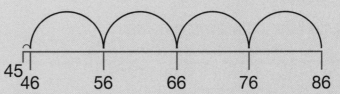

Draw number lines to work out these subtraction sums.

1. 75 − 32 =
2. 48 − 37 =
3. 39 − 26 =
4. 55 − 44 =
5. 41 − 21 =
6. 79 − 45 =
7. 88 − 63 =
8. 97 − 64 =

Draw number lines to work out these subtraction sums.

1. 54 − 39 =
2. 97 − 61 =
3. 92 − 68 =
4. 72 − 49 =
5. 65 − 58 =
6. 170 − 38 =
7. 155 − 41 =
8. 129 − 18 =

Draw number lines to work out these subtraction sums.

1. 953 − 431 =
2. 631 − 428 =
3. 557 − 296 =
4. 684 − 493 =
5. 721 − 583 =
6. 507 − 329 =
7. 417 − 256 =
8. 624 − 409 =

Training Tips

● **With subtraction the number gets smaller so check your answers!**

Finding the difference between two numbers

If you are asked to find the difference between two numbers, the numbers can be in any order.

Number lines are a really useful tool for working out differences.

Example

To find the difference between 15 and 38 you can use a number line. The total between the numbers is 23.

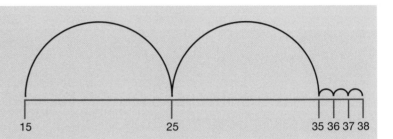

15   25   35 36 37 38

Bronze

What is the difference between these numbers? Try some without using number lines!

1. 12 and 28
2. 20 and 39
3. 5 and 27
4. 13 and 48
5. 28 and 34
6. 17 and 22
7. 25 and 29

Silver

What is the difference between these numbers? Try some without using number lines!

1. 38 and 72
2. 41 and 90
3. 27 and 84
4. 39 and 61
5. 82 and 79
6. 98 and 105
7. 67 and 75

Gold

What is the difference between these numbers? Try some without using number lines!

1. 127 and 183
2. 205 and 279
3. 190 and 263
4. 451 and 281
5. 365 and 372
6. 496 and 508
7. 764 and 751

Training Tips

● **It doesn't matter what order the numbers are in. The difference between 45 and 21 is the same as the difference between 21 and 45.**

Missing numbers

Sometimes the answer you need is not at the end of the sum but somewhere in the middle. Drawing a number line can be a useful way of working these out.

Example

$26 + \square = 42$

You need to find the difference between 26 and 42.
The number line shows that the missing number is 16.

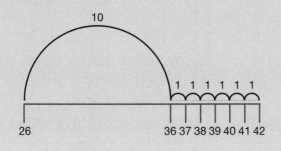

Example

$38 - \square = 15$

What must be taken away from 38 to leave 15?
23 needs to be taken away from 38 to leave 15.

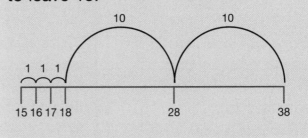

Bronze

Draw number lines to work out these missing numbers.

1. $\square + 18 = 37$

2. $\square + 15 = 30$

3. $\square - 12 = 19$

4. $\square - 22 = 42$

Silver

Draw number lines to work out these missing numbers.

1. $\square + 34 = 47$

2. $\square + 28 = 41$

3. $\square - 21 = 68$

4. $91 - \square = 60$

Gold

Draw number lines to work out these missing numbers.

1. $\square + 201 = 741$

2. $231 + \square = 403$

3. $\square - 121 = 357$

4. $\square - 284 = 711$

Training Tips

- **Add on or take away any jumps of ten before you work out the units.**

- **You can check your answers by doing an inverse sum.**

Understanding multiplication

Sports Shop Price List

T-shirts	£4	Sweatshirts	£8	Cap	£3
Tracksuit	£10	Football	£3	Bat	£7
Gloves	£6	Badge	£1	Socks	£2

Bronze

Work out how much it would cost to buy these items from the sports shop.
Write each one as a multiplication sum.

For example, 5 footballs is 5 × £3 = £15

1. 4 pairs of socks
2. 3 caps
3. 2 tracksuits

Work out how many of the following you could buy with £20.

4. tracksuits
5. badges
6. footballs

Silver

Work out how much it would cost to buy these items from the sports shop.
Write each one as a multiplication sum.

For example, 5 footballs is 5 × £3 = £15

1. 4 t-shirts
2. 8 footballs
3. 10 pairs of socks

Work out how many of the following you could buy with £20.

4. t-shirts
5. footballs
6. sweatshirts

Gold

Work out how much it would cost to buy these items from the sports shop.
Write each one as a multiplication sum.

For example, 5 footballs is 5 × £3 = £15

1. 6 pairs of gloves
2. 13 tracksuits
3. 20 pairs of socks

Work out how many of the following you could buy with £20.

4. caps and socks
5. footballs and bats
6. badges and gloves

Training Tips

- **Multiplication is the same as repeated addition.**

  So 5 × 3 = 3 + 3 + 3 + 3 + 3 = 15

Multiplication facts

Bronze

See how quickly you can answer these multiplication facts. Try to learn them.

1. $2 \times 2 =$

2. $3 \times 10 =$

3. $2 \times 10 =$

4. $7 \times 2 =$

5. $4 \times 2 =$

6. $10 \times 10 =$

7. $1 \times 10 =$

8. $2 \times 1 =$

Use the facts you know to work out the missing numbers.

9. $3 \times \square = 6$

10. $7 \times \square = 14$

11. $\square \times 10 = 60$

12. $\square \times 2 = 18$

13. $\square \times 10 = 100$

Silver

See how quickly you can answer these multiplication facts. Try to learn them.

1. $10 \times 5 =$

2. $3 \times 3 =$

3. $2 \times 10 =$

4. $4 \times 5 =$

5. $2 \times 8 =$

6. $7 \times 10 =$

7. $10 \times 10 =$

8. $9 \times 2 =$

Use the facts you know to work out the missing numbers.

9. $\square \times 2 = 18$

10. $3 \times \square = 9$

11. $10 \times \square = 0$

12. $\square \times 5 = 30$

13. $10 \times \square = 100$

Gold

See how quickly you can answer these multiplication facts. Try to learn them.

1. $6 \times 3 =$

2. $10 \times 7 =$

3. $12 \times 2 =$

4. $9 \times 3 =$

5. $11 \times 10 =$

6. $0 \times 3 =$

7. $8 \times 4 =$

8. $7 \times 5 =$

Use the facts you know to work out the missing numbers.

9. $9 \times \square = 45$

10. $10 \times \square = 10$

11. $8 \times \square = 32$

12. $\square \times 9 = 27$

13. $\square \times 10 = 110$

Training Tips

- A whole number multiplied by 10 always ends in zero.
- A whole number multiplied by 2 is always even.

Division by grouping

Different sports need teams of different sizes. The coaches need to work out how many teams there will be for each sport.

For example, 20 people in groups of four makes five teams. Look at the picture.

Bronze

Can you work out how many teams there will be for each sport?

1. Hockey – 12 people in groups of 3

2. Table tennis – 16 people in groups of 4

3. Long jump – 10 people in groups of 5

4. Rugby – 18 people in groups of 9

5. Darts – 8 people in groups of 2

6. Table football – 12 people in groups of 4

7. Javelin – 15 people in groups of 3

8. Gymnastics – 20 people in groups of 5

Silver

Can you work out how many teams there will be for each sport?

1. Long jump – 20 people in teams of 4

2. Relay running – 18 people in teams of 3

3. Swimming – 35 people in teams of 5

4. Badminton – 24 people in teams of 4

5. Squash – 32 people in teams of 4

6. High jump – 22 people in teams of 2

7. Football – 44 people in teams of 11

8. Karate – 20 people in teams of 5

Gold

Can you work out how many teams there will be for each sport?

1. Tennis – 36 people in teams of 4

2. Judo – 45 people in teams of 5

3. Rugby – 54 people in teams of 9

4. Discus – 27 people in teams of 3

5. Rowing – 44 people in teams of 4

6. Relay races – 65 people in teams of 5

7. Triple jump – 30 people in teams of 6

8. Netball – 36 people in teams of 4

Training Tips

- Division is the same as repeated subtraction.
  $20 \div 4$ is $20 - 4 - 4 - 4 - 4 - 4$
  So $20 \div 4 = 5$ (5 lots of 4)

Division by sharing

Another way of dividing is by sharing.

Example
$12 \div 3$ 12 shared between 3 is 4 each.

Bronze

Now try these:

1. $16 \div 4 =$

2. $15 \div 3 =$

3. $20 \div 2 =$

4. $9 \div 3 =$

Fill in the missing numbers to complete these division sums.

5. $12 \div \square = 3$

6. $9 \div \square = 3$

7. $8 \div \square = 4$

8. $24 \div \square = 6$

Silver

Now try these:

1. $30 \div 6 =$

2. $40 \div 4 =$

3. $27 \div 3 =$

4. $35 \div 5 =$

Fill in the missing numbers to complete these division sums.

5. $35 \div \square = 7$

6. $70 \div \square = 7$

7. $24 \div \square = 6$

8. $\square \div 5 = 9$

Gold

Now try these:

1. $44 \div 4 =$

2. $65 \div 5 =$

3. $120 \div 10 =$

4. $32 \div 4 =$

Fill in the missing numbers to complete these division sums.

5. $32 \div \square = 8$

6. $21 \div \square = 7$

7. $240 \div \square = 24$

8. $50 \div \square = 25$

Training Tips

- **Dividing by two is the same as halving.**

Division facts

Bronze

Silver

Gold

Try these:

1. $8 \div 2 =$
2. $60 \div 10 =$
3. $12 \div 2 =$
4. $20 \div 10 =$
5. $20 \div 5 =$
6. $90 \div 10 =$
7. $35 \div 5 =$
8. $18 \div 2 =$

Use the facts you know to work out the missing numbers.

9. $10 \div \square = 5$
10. $40 \div \square = 4$
11. $30 \div \square = 6$
12. $18 \div \square = 9$
13. $25 \div \square = 5$

Try these:

1. $90 \div 10 =$
2. $18 \div 2 =$
3. $15 \div 3 =$
4. $110 \div 10 =$
5. $12 \div 2 =$
6. $8 \div 4 =$
7. $9 \div 3 =$
8. $10 \div 10 =$

Use the facts you know to work out the missing numbers.

9. $12 \div \square = 4$
10. $45 \div \square = 9$
11. $100 \div \square = 10$
12. $18 \div \square = 9$
13. $21 \div \square = 7$

Try these:

1. $15 \div 3 =$
2. $36 \div 4 =$
3. $18 \div 9 =$
4. $22 \div 2 =$
5. $150 \div 10 =$
6. $10 \div 10 =$
7. $5 \div 1 =$
8. $21 \div 3 =$

Use the facts you know to work out the missing numbers.

9. $36 \div \square = 9$
10. $35 \div \square = 7$
11. $10 \div \square = 1$
12. $21 \div \square = 7$
13. $22 \div \square = 11$

Training Tips

- Use your times tables to help you work out division sums.

$4 \times 5 = 20$ so $20 \div 5 = 4$

Division with remainders

Sometimes numbers do not divide exactly and there are remainders.

$16 \div 3 = 5$ remainder 1

Bronze

Work out these division sums and show the remainders.

1. $10 \div 3 =$

2. $14 \div 4 =$

3. $8 \div 3 =$

4. $17 \div 5 =$

5. $9 \div 2 =$

6. $32 \div 10 =$

7. $20 \div 3 =$

8. $18 \div 5 =$

Silver

Work out these division sums and show the remainders.

1. $22 \div 4 =$

2. $45 \div 10 =$

3. $23 \div 2 =$

4. $68 \div 10 =$

5. $17 \div 3 =$

6. $24 \div 5 =$

7. $31 \div 4 =$

8. $33 \div 5 =$

Gold

Work out these division sums and show the remainders.

1. $34 \div 4 =$

2. $146 \div 10 =$

3. $35 \div 2 =$

4. $49 \div 5 =$

5. $29 \div 3 =$

6. $41 \div 2 =$

7. $78 \div 10 =$

8. $25 \div 4 =$

Training Tips

● The remainder must be smaller than the number you are dividing by. Check your answers!

Rounding up or down

Sometimes when dividing numbers to solve a problem there is a remainder. You may need to decide whether to round the answer up or down depending on what the problem is asking.

Let's have a look…

Tickets cost £5 each and Tom has £37 to spend. How many can he buy?

37 ÷ 5 = 7 remainder 2

This answer must be rounded down to 7, as Tom does not have enough money for 8 tickets.

Sita has 23 cakes. Each box holds 4 cakes. How many boxes does she need?

23 ÷ 4 = 5 remainder 3

This answer must be rounded up to 6 to make sure all the cakes are in a box.

Bronze

Now try these:

1. There are 16 cakes and 5 children. How many can they each have?

2. How many strips of 10cm ribbon can be cut from 63cm?

3. Juice cartons are sold in packs of 4. Sophie needs 30. How many packs must she buy?

4. There can be no more than 3 flowers in each vase. Sonny has 17 flowers. How many vases will he need?

5. At the end of a party 37 balloons are shared between 10 children. How many do they each get?

6. Amy needs 85p to buy a comic. She saves 10p a week. How many weeks will it take her to buy her comic?

Training Tips

● **Make sure your answer is sensible and you have rounded the right way.**

● **Multiplication is the opposite operation. Use it to check your answers.**

Now try these:

1. Tickets cost £3 each. Beth has £19. How many can she buy?

2. There are 43 children. A table seats 5. How many tables are needed?

3. Juice cartons are sold in packs of 4. Sophie needs 41. How many packs must she buy?

4. There can be no more than 3 flowers in each vase. Sonny has 32 flowers. How many vases will he need?

5. There are 33 children. How many teams of 5 can be made? How many children are not able to join in?

6. Amy needs £1.25 to buy a comic. She saves 10p a week. How many weeks will it take her to buy her comic?

Now try these:

1. There are 73 children. A table seats 5. How many tables are needed?

2. Juice cartons are sold in packs of 4. Sophie needs 79. How many packs must she buy?

3. There can be no more than 3 flowers in each vase. Sonny has 61 flowers. How many vases will he need?

4. At the end of a party 187 balloons are shared between 10 children. How many do they each get?

5. There are 68 children. How many teams of 5 can be made? How many children are not able to join in?

6. Amy needs £2.20 to buy a comic. She saves 25p a week. How many weeks will it take her to buy her comic?

Multiplying and dividing by 10

A quick and easy way to multiply by 10 is to move each digit one place to the left and put zero into the units column.

The same rule applies for dividing but you need to move each digit one place to the right and take off the zero.

T	U		H	T	U
7	6	× 10 becomes	7	6	0

H	T	U		T	U
5	4	0	÷ 10 becomes	5	4

Bronze

Multiply by 10:

1. 7

2. 9

3. 26

4. 10

Divide by 10:

5. 80

6. 60

7. 170

8. 240

Silver

Multiply by 10:

1. 79

2. 90

3. 348

4. 601

Divide by 10:

5. 860

6. 450

7. 5000

8. 3040

Gold

Multiply:

1. 54 × 10 =

2. 90 × 10 =

3. 147 × 100 =

4. 658 × 10 =

Divide:

5. 850 ÷ 10 =

6. 6500 ÷ 100 =

7. 7400 ÷ 10 =

8. 9700 ÷ 100 =

Training Tips

- A whole number multiplied by 10 always ends in zero.

Putting it into practice

Some of the scores have fallen off the judge's scoreboard.

Japan	10	Norway	
England	90	Scotland	
Turkey		Switzerland	600
Australia		Finland	21
Holland		Canada	2000
Hong Kong		Denmark	8

Bronze

See if you can solve the clues below to fill in the missing scores.

1. Norway scored 8 times as much as Japan.

2. Divide England's score by 10 to find Turkey's score.

Silver

See if you can solve the clues below to fill in the missing scores.

1. Australia scored 100 times as much as Denmark.

2. Scotland scored one tenth of Switzerland.

Gold

See if you can solve the clues below to fill in the missing scores.

1. Holland scored ten times as much as Finland.

2. Divide Canada's score by 100 to find Hong Kong's score.

Training Tips

● **Write down each new fact as you get it.**

Word problems

Question: There are 100 books on a shelf. 45 of them are fiction, 25 are information books and the rest are poetry books. How many are poetry books?

1. The first thing to do is to think about what the problem is telling you. Which operations do we need to use? Add the numbers? Subtract? Multiply or divide? Or do we need to use more than one operation?

2. This problem needs addition and subtraction. Let's look.

3. We know there are 100 books altogether so…

fiction + information + poetry = 100
fiction + information = 45 + 25 = 70

The rest are poetry. 100 − 70 = 30

Answer: There must be 30 poetry books.

Bronze

Look at the problems and decide which operation to use. Work out the answers and show your sum.

1. Two children have 12 pencils each. How many do they have altogether?

2. In her pocket Lisa has two 10p coins, three pennies and one 5p coin. How much money does she have?

3. There are 28 biscuits on a plate. If two children share them equally how many will they each have?

4. Crayons are sold in packs of 5. If Amit has 6 packs, how many crayons does he have?

5. There are 34 sweets in a packet. Joel eats 13. How many are left?

Training Tips

● **Read each problem very carefully and think about what it says. It might help to draw a picture or talk about it with a friend.**

Look at the problems and decide which operation to use. Work out the answers and show your sum.

1. A box holds 35 nuts. How many are there in 3 boxes?

2. There are 60 coloured pencils in the box. 26 are red, 23 are blue and the rest are green. How many green pencils are there?

3. I think of a number and double it and add 5. The answer is 45. What was my number?

4. In the garden Sophie saw 3 spiders, 7 birds and 5 cats. How many legs did she see on the animals?

5. There are 31 people on the bus. 16 get on and 20 get off. How many people are now on the bus?

Look at the problems and decide which operation to use. Work out the answers and show your sum.

1. There are 78 books on the top shelf and 42 on the bottom shelf. I take 29 of them away. How many are left?

2. A beetle has 6 legs. How many legs do 9 beetles have?

3. Tom has 27 cars. Jamie has twice as many. How many do they have altogether?

4. In the garden Sophie saw 10 spiders, 15 birds and 5 cats. How many legs did she see on the animals?

5. There are 36 children in the class. Half of them have packed lunch. 10 children have school dinners and the rest go home. How many children go home for lunch?

Training Tips

● **Check your answers by doing the problem again or doing the opposite operation.**

37

Number puzzles

What numbers can you make using the numbers 4, 10 and 5 and the × + and = signs?

$4 \times 10 = 40$	$5 + 4 = 9$	$4 + 5 + 10 = 19$
$4 \times 5 = 20$	$4 + 10 = 14$	
$5 \times 10 = 50$	$5 + 10 = 15$	

Bronze

Try these:

1. Fill in the missing signs:

   $16 * 2 = 8$

   $21 * 14 = 35$

   $4 * 5 = 20$

   $30 * 17 = 13$

2. Find five different ways to add odd numbers to make 15.

3. Find three pairs of numbers with a difference of 5 and a total greater than 20.

4. Use 1, 4 and 5 and + − and = . How many different numbers can you make?

Silver

Try these:

1. Fill in the missing signs:

   $73 * 88 = 161$

   $160 * 41 = 119$

   $7 * 8 = 56$

   $95 * 5 = 19$

2. Find five different ways to add odd numbers to make 45.

3. Find a pair of numbers with a difference of 5 and a total less than 20.

4. Make a triangle shape using the numbers 1 to 6 so that the sum of each side of the triangle is 12.

Gold

Try these:

1. Fill in the missing signs and numbers:

   $120 * ? = 12$

   $30 * ? = 46$

   $45 * ? = 9$

   $50 * ? = 24$

2. Find a pair of numbers with a difference of 11 and a total of 35.

3. Find five different ways to add odd numbers to make 75.

4. Make a triangle shape using the numbers 1 to 6 so that the sum of each side of the triangle is the same.

5. Find a pair of numbers with a difference of 5 and a total between 15 and 20.

Training Tips

- **The way to solve some of these problems is by guessing first.**

Finding totals

Sports Café

SALAD	£2.20	**PASTA**	£6.50	**COFFEE**	75p
PIZZA	£1.60	**CURRY**	£7.20	**TEA**	80p
FISH	£3.50	**SANDWICH**	£1.05	**COLA**	50p
CHICKEN	£2.80	**HOT DOG**	£1.25	**LEMONADE**	40p

 **Bronze**

How much would the following cost?

1. A sandwich and a cola
2. Hot dog and a salad
3. Fish and a salad
4. Salad and a coffee
5. Two sandwiches

What can you buy for:

6. £4?
7. £3?
8. £2?

 Silver

How much would the following cost?

1. Pasta and fish
2. Chicken and a salad
3. Pasta and a coffee
4. Curry and a cola
5. Two pizzas

What can you buy for:

6. £8?
7. £7?
8. £10?

 **Gold**

How much would the following cost?

1. Pasta and chicken
2. Two curries
3. Pizza, salad and a coffee
4. A sandwich, a hot dog and a pizza
5. Three chickens

What can you buy for:

6. £15?
7. £20?
8. £10.50?

 *Training Tips*

- When working out totals add up the pounds first then the pence.

Money problems

Sports Shop

T-shirts	£4.50	Sweatshirts	£8	Cap	£5.25
Tracksuit	£10.75	Football	£3	Bat	£7.50
Gloves	£6	Badge	£1	Socks	£2

Jo saves 20p a week. How long will it take for her to be able to afford a pair of socks?

Jo saves 20p in one week, so in two weeks she will have 40p. In three weeks she will have 60p. She needs 200p.

So, ☐ × 20 = 200. It must be 10.
It will take Jo 10 weeks to save enough for the socks.

Bronze

Try these.

1. Amrit saves 50p a week. How many weeks must he save to buy a football?

2. Saul buys a T-shirt. How much change will he get from £10?

3. Luke buys a bat. He gives the shopkeeper a £10 note. What coins will he get in his change?

4. Ella buys two sweatshirts. She pays with two notes and one coin. What were they?

5. Pete has £10 to spend. What two items could he buy?

Training Tips

- If the answer is money don't forget to write the £ or the p sign.

Try these.

1. Priya saves 20p a week. How long will it take her to afford a T-shirt?

2. Saul buys a tracksuit. How much change will he get from £20?

3. Luke buys a cap. He gives the shopkeeper a £10 note. What coins will he get in his change?

4. Ella buys two T-shirts. She pays with one note and eight coins. What were they?

5. How many tracksuits can be bought for £50?

Try these.

1. Sam saves £1 a month. How long must he save to afford a tracksuit and a T-shirt?

2. Rebecca buys three tracksuits. How much change will she get from £50?

3. Ella buys two caps. She pays with two notes and five coins. What were they?

4. Pete spends exactly £16. What two items did he buy?

5. Jordan buys a cap. He uses 6 coins to pay for it. What could they be?

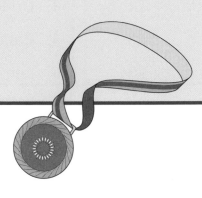

Calculating change

Drawing number lines is a good way to calculate change.

Example

Sanjiv bought cola that cost 75p. He gave the waitress £2. How much was his change?

His change was
5p + 10p + 10p + £1 = £1.25

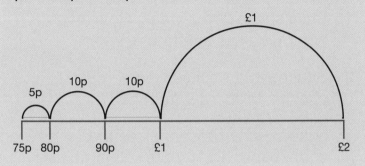

Sports Café

SALAD £2.20	**SANDWICH** £1.05
PIZZA £1.60	**HOT DOG** £1.25
FISH £3.50	**COFFEE** 75p
CHICKEN £2.80	**TEA** 80p
PASTA £6.50	**COLA** 50p
CURRY £7.20	**LEMONADE** 40p

Bronze

Calculate the change when the following items are bought with the amount shown.

1. Tea — £1
2. Pizza — £2
3. Lemonade — £1
4. Chicken — £3
5. Salad — £3

Silver

Calculate the change when the following items are bought with the amount shown.

1. Sandwich — £2
2. Curry — £10
3. Coffee — £2
4. Pasta — £10
5. Lemonade — £2

Gold

Calculate the change when the following items are bought with the amount shown.

1. Two pizzas — £10
2. Hot dog and tea — £10
3. Two curries — £20
4. Pasta and coffee — £10
5. Fish and salad — £20

Training Tips

● **Count up to the nearest pound to calculate the pence and then count up the pounds.**

Measuring length

Short lengths can be measured in cm or mm.
1 cm is the same as 10 mm.

Let's practise drawing some lines.
Remember to use a ruler and to start at zero.
Make sure they are all straight!

Draw lines that are these lengths:

1. 8 cm
2. 12 cm
3. $6\frac{1}{2}$ cm
4. 9 cm
5. $5\frac{1}{2}$ cm
6. $3\frac{1}{2}$ cm
7. 14 cm
8. $2\frac{1}{2}$ cm

Draw lines that are these lengths:

1. 15 cm
2. $12\frac{1}{2}$ cm
3. $9\frac{1}{2}$ cm
4. $\frac{1}{2}$ cm
5. 70 mm
6. 45 mm
7. 16 cm
8. 85 mm

Use some squared paper. Draw rectangles that have sides these lengths:

1. 5 cm and 8 cm
2. 70 mm and 30 mm
3. 2 cm and 90 mm
4. $4\frac{1}{2}$ cm and 6 cm
5. 75 mm and 45 mm
6. 60 mm and $3\frac{1}{2}$ cm
7. 100 mm and 10 cm
8. $5\frac{1}{2}$ cm and $8\frac{1}{2}$ cm

Training Tips

- When using a ruler, make sure the line starts at zero.
- 10 mm = 1 cm
  5 mm = $\frac{1}{2}$ cm

Length problems

Length is measured in millimetres (mm), centimetres (cm), metres (m) or kilometres (km).

1 cm = 10 mm	1 m = 100 cm	1 km = 1000 m

Bronze

Fill in the missing numbers to make these correct:

1. 3 cm = ☐ mm

2. 5 m = ☐ cm

3. 1 m 50 cm = ☐ cm

Try these problems:

4. My cat is 25 cm tall. My dog is 15 cm taller. How tall is my dog?

5. I am 1 m 5 cm tall. My dad is twice as tall. How tall is he?

Silver

Fill in the missing numbers to make these correct:

1. 8 cm = ☐ mm

2. 12 m = ☐ cm

3. 2.5 m = ☐ cm

Try these problems:

4. It is 7 km from Tom's house to Jane's. Fred lives another 5 km away. How far is it to Fred's house? How many m?

5. How many 10 cm pieces of ribbon can I cut from $2\frac{1}{2}$ m?

Gold

Fill in the missing numbers to make these correct:

1. 3.05 m = ☐ cm

2. 150 cm = ☐ m

3. 8 km = ☐ m

Try these problems:

4. I am digging a tunnel that is 5 m long. I have dug 2 m 25 cm so far. How much further do I have to go?

5. A garden is rectangular. The short sides measure 8 m. The long sides are twice as long. How much fence will I need to go all the way round?

Training Tips

- 10 mm = 1 cm
- 100 cm = 1 m
- 1000 m = 1 km

Mass problems

The mass or weight of an object is measured in grams (g) or kilograms (kg).

$$1 \text{ kg} = 1000 \text{ g}$$

Bronze

Fill in the missing numbers to make these correct:

1. 3 kg = ☐ g

2. 6000 g = ☐ kg

3. 1000 g = ☐ kg

Try these problems:

4. A box contains 5 kg of potatoes. How many boxes are needed for 20 kg?

5. A bag of sugar weighs 200 g. How much would 4 bags weigh?

6. Mark weighed 4 kg when he was born. He is now twice as heavy. How much does he weigh?

Silver

Fill in the missing numbers to make these correct:

1. 7 kg = ☐ g

2. 4500 g = ☐ kg

3. $2\frac{1}{2}$ kg = ☐ g

Try these problems:

4. Sally bought 100 g of sweets. She ate a quarter of them. How much does she have left?

5. Joe weighs 17 kg. His dad weighs twice as much. How much do they weigh together?

6. An apple weighs about 50 g. How many apples will you get in 1 kg?

Gold

Fill in the missing numbers to make these correct:

1. 3500 g = ☐ kg

2. $7\frac{1}{4}$ kg = ☐ g

3. 5250 g = ☐ kg

Try these problems:

4. Joe weighs 26 kg. His dad weighs twice as much. How much do they weigh together?

5. Sally bought 1 kg of bananas. She ate a quarter of them and gave 300 g to her friend. How much does she have left?

6. An apple weighs about 50 g. How many apples will you get in $1\frac{1}{2}$ kg?

Training Tips

- 1000 g = 1 kg
- 250 g = $\frac{1}{4}$ kg
- 500 g = $\frac{1}{2}$ kg
- 750 g = $\frac{3}{4}$ kg

Measuring mass

The mass of an object tells us how much it weighs.
Light objects can be measured in grams (g).
Heavy objects are measured using kilograms (kg).

1 kilogram = 1000 grams

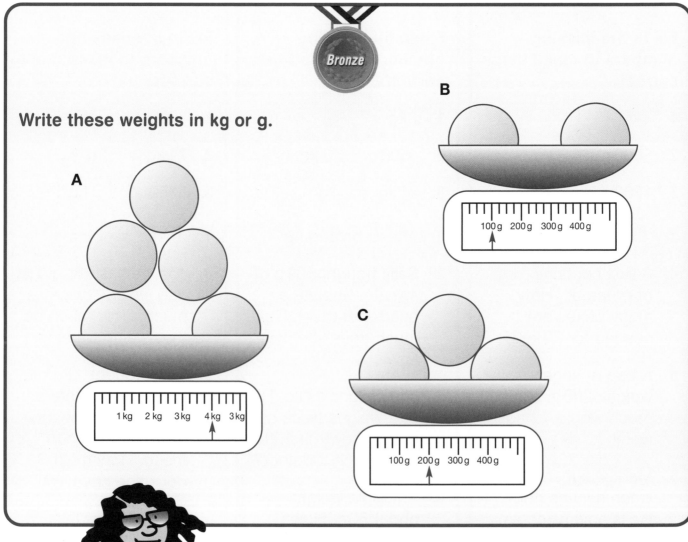

Write these weights in kg or g.

A

B — 100g 200g 300g 400g

C — 100g 200g 300g 400g

A — 1kg 2kg 3kg 4kg 3kg

Training Tips

● Reading scales is like reading a clock. The numbers and the pointer go the same way round. If the pointer is between two numbers look to see which one it has gone past.

Write these weights in kg or g.

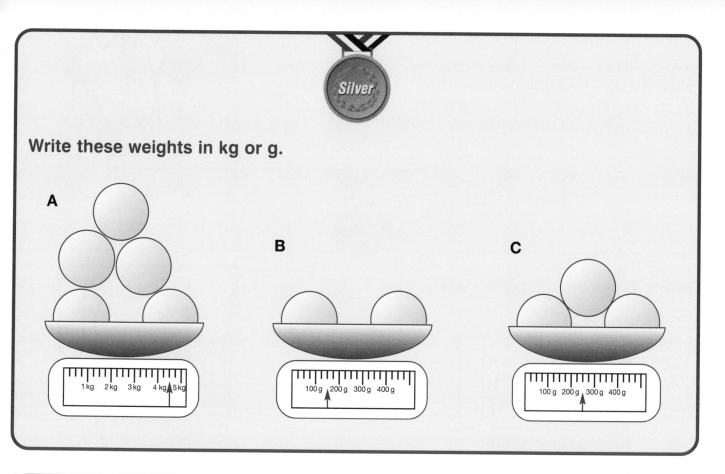

A

B

C

Write these weights in kg or g.

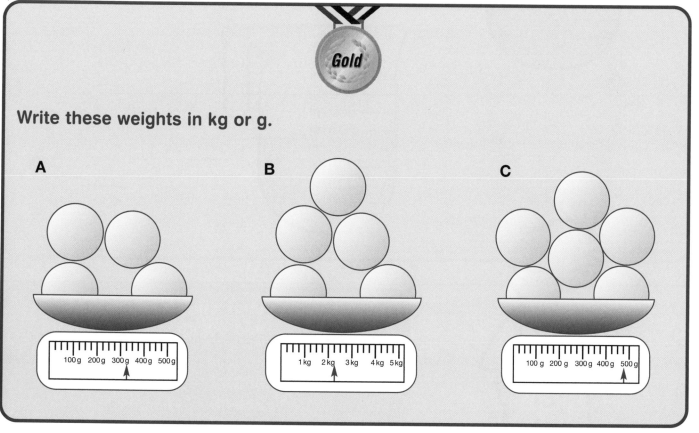

A

B

C

Measuring capacity

Capacity is measured in litres (l) and millilitres (ml).

There are 1000 ml in one litre.

Bronze

Write these capacities in l or ml.

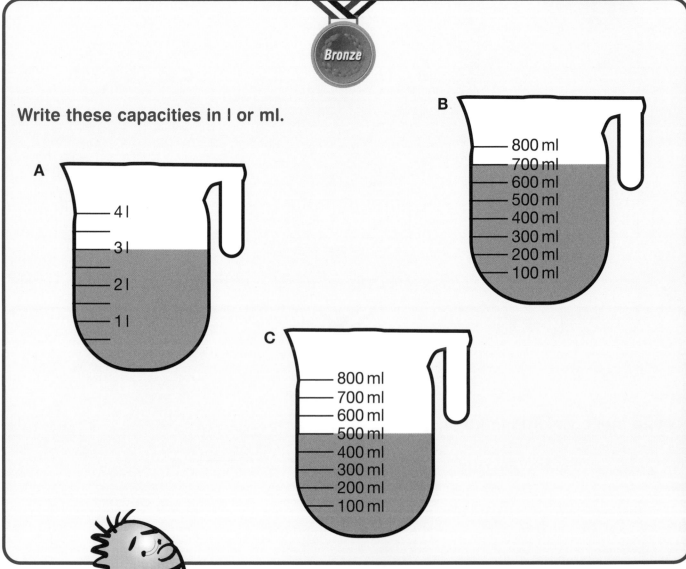

A
- 4 l
- 3 l
- 2 l
- 1 l

B
- 800 ml
- 700 ml
- 600 ml
- 500 ml
- 400 ml
- 300 ml
- 200 ml
- 100 ml

C
- 800 ml
- 700 ml
- 600 ml
- 500 ml
- 400 ml
- 300 ml
- 200 ml
- 100 ml

Training Tips

- Look closely at the scale and decide if it is in ml or l.
- 1000 ml = 1 l
  500 ml = $\frac{1}{2}$ l
  250 ml = $\frac{1}{4}$ l

Write these capacities in l or ml.

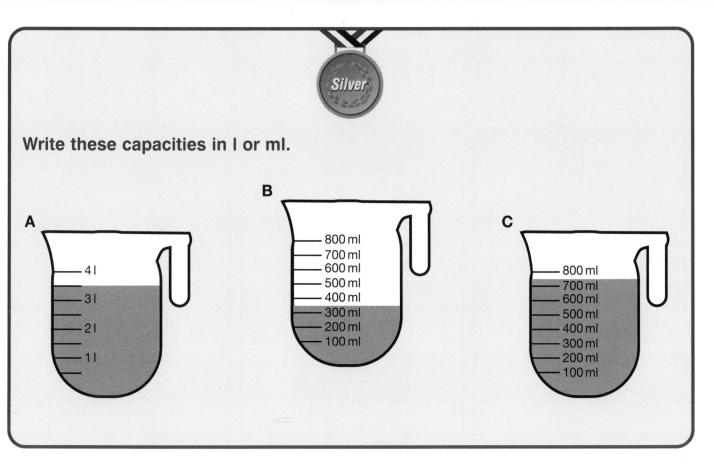

Write these capacities in l or ml.

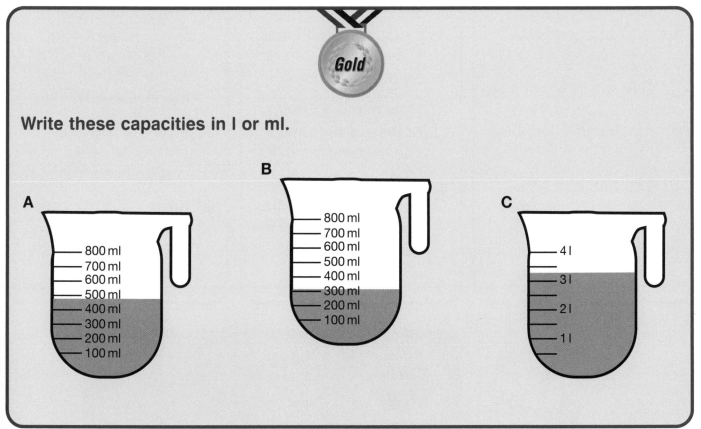

Capacity problems

The capacity of a liquid is measured in litres (l) and millilitres (ml).

> 1 l = 1000 ml

Bronze

Fill in the missing numbers to make these correct:

1. 7 l = ☐ ml

2. 4000 ml = ☐ l

3. 6000 ml = ☐ l

Try these:

4. How many 200 ml bottles of perfume can be filled from 1 l?

5. A bottle of lemonade holds 100 ml. How much can 17 bottles hold?

6. The bottle of cola held 1 l. Ella drank 400 ml. How much was left?

Silver

Fill in the missing numbers to make these correct:

1. 6 l = ☐ ml

2. 7500 ml = ☐ l

3. $5\frac{1}{2}$ l = ☐ ml

Try these:

4. Steven took 15 ml of medicine three times a day. How much did he take in 2 days?

5. How many 100 ml bottles of perfume can be filled from $1\frac{1}{2}$ l?

6. Kenny had buckets holding 2 l, 1500 ml and $4\frac{1}{2}$ l. How much water did he have?

Gold

Fill in the missing numbers to make these correct:

1. 10 l = ☐ ml

2. 7500 ml = ☐ l

3. $4\frac{1}{2}$ l = ☐ ml

Try these:

4. The bottle of cola held 1 l. Ella drank half and gave 150 ml to her brother. How much was left?

5. How many 50 ml bottles of perfume can be filled from $\frac{1}{4}$ l?

6. Kenny had buckets holding $1\frac{1}{2}$ l, 250 ml and $1\frac{1}{2}$ l. How much water did he have?

Training Tips

- 1000 ml = 1 l
- 250 ml = $\frac{1}{4}$ l
- 500 ml = $\frac{1}{2}$ l
- 750 ml = $\frac{3}{4}$ l

Choosing units

The units of measurement we have learned are:

ml   l   g   kg   mm   cm   m   km

Bronze

For each of the measurements below decide which units have been used.

1. A toy car weighs 300 ☐

2. George is 96 ☐ tall

3. A glass held 300 ☐ of milk

4. The ladybird was 9 ☐ long

5. Lucy weighed 12 ☐

6. The bath held 36 ☐ of water

Silver

For each of the measurements below decide which units have been used.

1. Sam bought 100 ☐ of sweets

2. My page is 21 ☐ wide

3. This melon weighs more than 2 ☐

4. I have to take 5 ☐ of medicine every day

5. My toy car is 90 ☐ long

6. Our playground is $\frac{1}{2}$ ☐ wide

Gold

For each of the measurements below decide which units have been used.

1. An apple weighs about 50 ☐

2. My shoelaces are 30 ☐ long

3. I need $\frac{1}{2}$ ☐ of potatoes for dinner

4. The playground is $1\frac{1}{2}$ ☐ long

5. This pencil is 150 ☐ long

6. I can jump nearly 1 ☐

Training Tips

- If something is light it will only be a few grams.

- If something is very small it is probably measured in mm.

Negative numbers (temperature)

When it gets very cold the temperature drops below 0 degrees. We then read the scale in negative numbers. Negative numbers go back from zero. We write temperatures as °C.

Bronze

Look at the thermometers below and write the temperature shown.

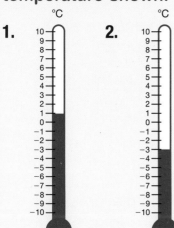

1.   **2.**

Draw thermometers from −10°C to 0°C. Show:

3. −9 degrees

4. −3 degrees

5. 0 degrees

Silver

Look at the thermometers below and write the temperature shown.

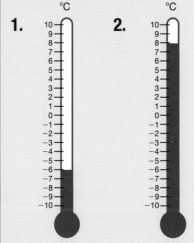

1.   **2.**

Draw thermometers from −5°C to 5°C. Show:

3. −3 degrees

4. 3 degrees

5. 0 degrees

Gold

Look at the thermometers below and write the temperature shown.

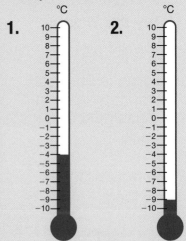

1.   **2.**

Draw thermometers from −10°C to 10°C. Mark the scale in twos. Show:

3. −8 degrees

4. 6 degrees

5. 7 degrees

Training Tips

● When writing negative numbers, count backwards from zero instead of forwards.

Units of time

There are lots of units of time.

60 seconds = 1 minute	60 minutes = 1 hour	24 hours = 1 day
7 days = 1 week	12 months = 1 year	52 weeks = 1 year	365 days = 1 year

Bronze

Fill in the missing numbers to complete this information.

1. 2 weeks = ☐ days

2. One year = ☐ months

3. 60 seconds = ☐

4. 24 hours = ☐

5. 2 years = ☐ months

6. 1 year = ☐ days

7. 1 minute = ☐ seconds

8. 7 days = ☐

Silver

Fill in the missing numbers to complete this information.

1. 2 years = ☐ months

2. 4 weeks = ☐ days

3. 2 minutes = ☐ seconds

4. 72 hours = ☐ days

5. 2 years = ☐ weeks

6. 1 year = ☐ days

7. 1 month = about ☐ days

8. 10 hours = ☐ minutes

Gold

Fill in the missing numbers to complete this information.

1. $1\frac{1}{2}$ years = ☐ months

2. 6 weeks = ☐ days

3. 5 minutes = ☐ seconds

4. 3 days = ☐ hours

5. 2 years = ☐ days

6. 6 months = about ☐ days

7. A fortnight = ☐ days

8. $\frac{1}{6}$ hour = ☐ minutes

Training Tips

- In a leap year there are 366 days. 2008 and 2012 are leap years.

Reading times

We use two different types of clock to tell the time – an analogue clock and a digital clock.

These two clocks both show the same time.
It is 'forty minutes past five o'clock'.
A better way to say that is 'twenty to six'.

analogue *digital*

Bronze

Look at the clocks below and write in words the times they show.

1.

2. **5:45**

3. **2:00**

4. [analogue clock]

Show these times on an analogue clock and a digital clock.

5. half past three

6. eleven o'clock

7. half past nine

8. quarter past two

Silver

Look at the clocks below and write in words the times they show.

1.

2. **6:10**

3. **7:45**

4. [analogue clock]

Show these times on an analogue clock and a digital clock.

5. twelve o'clock

6. quarter to six

7. twenty past ten

8. five past eight

Gold

Look at the clocks below and write in words the times they show.

1.

2. **9:40**

3. **4:55**

4.

Show these times on an analogue clock and a digital clock.

5. five past one

6. twenty-five to seven

7. five to nine

8. ten to two

Training Tips

● When drawing the hands on an analogue clock, make sure the hand that shows the minutes is longer than the hand that shows the hours.

Time problems

Being a referee means solving lots of time problems.

See if you can help the referees solve these problems.

1. A hockey match started at ten o'clock and lasted for half an hour. What time did it finish?

2. A tennis game started at 2:30 and finished at 2:45. How long did it last?

3. The French swimming team practised from 11:45 until 12:15. How many minutes were they swimming for?

See if you can help the referees solve these problems.

1. A netball match started at 3:15pm and finished at five to four. How long did it last?

2. The long jump competition takes 50 minutes. If it finished at four o'clock, what time did it start?

3. The rugby match starts at half past ten. If it lasts for 80 minutes, what time will it end?

See if you can help the referees solve these problems.

1. The rugby match starts at quarter past ten. If it lasts for 80 minutes, what time will it end?

2. The rowing competition takes 2 hours and 25 minutes. It starts at half past nine. What time will it finish?

3. The gymnastics competition started at eight o'clock. There were three teams that each took an hour and a half. There were two breaks of 15 minutes each. What time did it finish?

Training Tips

● **Practise counting in fives. It will help you tell the time!**

2D shapes

2D shapes are flat shapes that can easily be drawn on paper.

They can be described by looking at the sides and the corners.

What shape has one curved side and no corners? … A circle!

 Bronze

Write some clues to describe these shapes and try them out on a friend.

1. triangle

2. circle

3. rectangle

Now draw some shapes using dotted paper and a ruler.

Draw 5 different shapes with 4 straight sides. Can you name any of them?

 Silver

Write some clues to describe these shapes and try them out on a friend.

1. pentagon

2. semicircle

3. hexagon

Now draw some shapes using dotted paper and a ruler.

Draw 5 different pentagons. Make sure all the sides are straight!

 Gold

Write some clues to describe these shapes and try them out on a friend.

1. star

2. octagon

3. semicircle

Now draw some shapes using dotted paper and a ruler.

Draw 5 different quadrilaterals with at least one right angle.

 **Training Tips**

- An octopus has 8 legs and an octagon has 8 sides.

- Hexagon has an x in it and so does six. A hexagon is the shape with six sides.

3D shapes

3D shapes are solid shapes that are not so easy to draw. To describe them we need to think about the faces, the edges and the vertices (corners).

A cube has 6 square faces. It has 8 vertices and 12 edges.

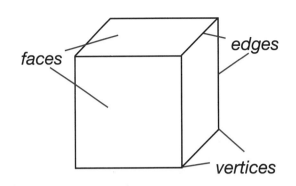

faces

edges

vertices

Bronze

Write some clues to describe these shapes. Remember to describe what the faces are like and how many edges and vertices they have.

1. cube

2. sphere

3. cylinder

4. cuboid

5. cone

6. pyramid

Silver

Write some clues to describe these shapes. Remember to describe what the faces are like and how many edges and vertices they have.

1. cube

2. pyramid

3. hemisphere

4. sphere

5. prism

6. cylinder

Gold

Write some clues to describe these shapes. Remember to describe what the faces are like and how many edges and vertices they have.

1. square-based pyramid

2. hemisphere

3. hexagonal prism

4. triangular-based pyramid

5. cube

6. triangular prism

Training Tips

- To help remember the names, think about objects that are the same shape, such as an ice cream cone and the pyramids in Egypt.

Lines of symmetry

A line of symmetry is like looking in a mirror. Both sides must be the same, like a reflection.

This triangle has only one line of symmetry but a rectangle has two.

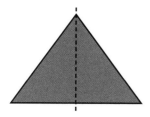 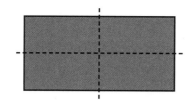

Copy the shapes below and draw in the lines of symmetry.

1.   2.

3.    4.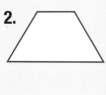

Copy the shapes below and draw in the lines of symmetry.

1.   2.

3.   4.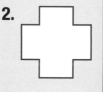

Copy the shapes below and draw in the lines of symmetry.

1.   2.

3.   4.

Training Tips
- **You could use a mirror to check before you draw.**

Position and direction

Look at the grid below. We can describe where things are by using letters and numbers. Always give the letter first!

Ant Hill is at E8.
Coconut Grove is at L5.

We can use the compass points **north**, **south**, **east** and **west** to give directions from one place to another.

For example, to get from Ant Hill to Faraway Lagoon, we need to go 5 squares north and 1 square west.

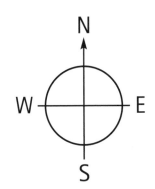

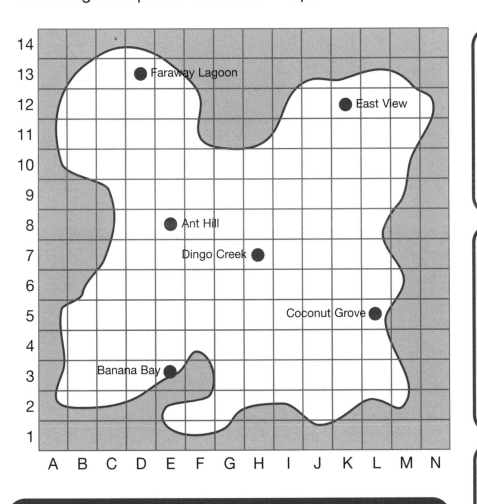

Training Tips
• When finding a location, always go along first and then up.

Bronze

Write directions to travel between Ant Hill and East View.

Silver

Write directions to travel from Ant Hill to Dingo Creek and then to Banana Bay.

Gold

Write directions to travel to each spot on the island starting at Ant Hill and ending at Faraway Lagoon.

Right angles

A quarter turn is also called a right angle.
Lots of 2D shapes have right angles in them.

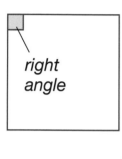

*right
angle*

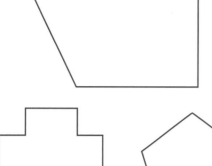

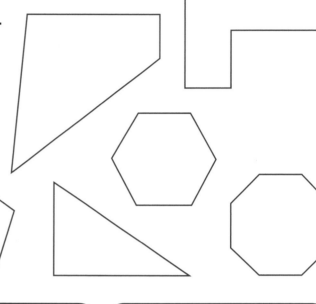

Bronze

Look at the shapes above.

1. Sort them into two groups:

    A Shapes with some right angles

    B Shapes with no right angles

2. Colour all the right angles red.

Silver

Look at the shapes above.

1. Sort them into three groups:

    A Shapes with all right angles

    B Shapes with some right angles

    C Shapes with no right angles

2. Colour all the right angles red.

Gold

Look at the shapes above.

1. Sort them into three groups. Some shapes may appear in more than one group:

    A Shapes with angles less than a right angle

    B Shapes with right angles

    C Shapes with angles greater than a right angle

2. Colour all the right angles red.

Training Tips

● **A straight line is made up of two right angles!**

Sorting information

The table below shows the scores from a rugby competition.

Japan 12	Norway 7	England 8	France 11	Spain 10
Switzerland 30	USA 25	Turkey 13	Denmark 14	Russia 16
Iceland 20	Australia 15	Scotland 17	Ireland 20	Greece 16
Finland 25	China 19	Hong Kong 19	Egypt 18	Morocco 45
Germany 35	Holland 24	Canada 60	South Africa 45	Austria 27
Wales 42	Poland 65	Mexico 28	Sweden 70	Brazil 95

Bronze

Copy this Carroll diagram and sort the scores into the correct places.

Multiples of 5	Not multiples of 5
Spain 10	Norway 7

1. How many scores were not multiples of 5?

2. What score was the highest multiple of 5?

3. What was the lowest score that was not a multiple of 5?

4. How many multiples of 5 were also greater than 40?

5. How many scores less than 40 were not multiples of 5?

Silver

Copy this Carroll diagram and sort the scores into the correct places.

Odd numbers	Even numbers

1. How many odd numbers were greater than 40?

2. List the even numbers less than 40.

3. How many scores were odd numbers?

4. How many scores were less than 40?

5. What was the highest even number scored?

Gold

Copy this Venn diagram and sort the scores into the correct places.

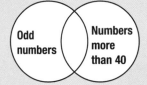

1. Which scores were odd numbers and also more than 40?

2. Which even numbers were more than 40?

3. Which odd numbers were less than 40?

4. How many teams scored more than 40?

5. List the numbers that did not fit in either circle. What did you notice about them?

Drawing bar charts

The table below shows the scores from a hockey competition.

Round 1		Round 2		Round 3	
Japan	7	Australia	12	Holland	40
Norway	12	Scotland	24	Canada	60
England	18	Ireland	15	Hong Kong	130
France	10	Switzerland	18	Austria	50
Spain	15	Greece	22	Wales	75
USA	9	Finland	28	Poland	135
Turkey	8	China	19	South Africa	95
Denmark	14	Egypt	9	Mexico	80
Russia	15	Morocco	14	Sweden	115
Iceland	11	Germany	23	Brazil	145

Bronze

Draw a bar chart for Round 1.

1. Which countries scored 15 points?

2. Which countries scored more than 10 points?

3. How many more points did Russia score than France?

4. How many fewer points did Iceland score than England?

5. Which countries scored an even number of points?

6. Which countries scored less than Norway?

7. How many more points did England score than the USA?

8. How many countries competed in Round 1?

Training Tips

● **Colour each bar a different colour to make it easier to read.**

Draw a bar chart for Round 2.

1. Which countries scored between 10 and 20 points?

2. Which countries scored more than 17 points?

3. How many more points did Greece score than Morocco?

4. How many fewer points did Egypt score than Scotland?

5. Which countries scored an odd number of points?

6. Which countries scored less than Switzerland?

7. How many more points did Finland score than Australia?

8. How many fewer points did China score than Germany?

Draw a bar chart for Round 3.

1. Which countries scored between 105 and 150 points?

2. Which countries scored less than 95 points?

3. How many more points did Hong Kong score than Holland?

4. How many fewer points did Mexico score than Sweden?

5. Which countries scored a multiple of 5?

6. Which countries scored more than Wales?

7. Which country scored twice as much as Holland?

8. Use the words most, least and difference to write three sentences about your bar chart.

Pictograms

A pictogram is a way of using pictures to show information.

All pictograms must have a key to show what each picture represents.

Draw pictograms to show how many medals each country won.

Key [bronze medal] = 1 medal

Japan	6
Norway	11
England	19
France	8
Spain	5
USA	11
Turkey	12
Denmark	14
Russia	10
Iceland	7

Draw pictograms to show how many medals each country won.

Key [silver medal] = 2 medals

Australia	18
Scotland	12
Ireland	16
Switzerland	9
Greece	15
Finland	14
China	7
Egypt	13
Morocco	16
Germany	10

Draw pictograms to show how many medals each country won.

Key [gold medal] = 4 medals

Holland	16
Canada	12
Hong Kong	20
Austria	10
Wales	18
Poland	14
South Africa	10
Mexico	6
Sweden	9
Brazil	17

- If [silver medal] = 2 medals

  then [half medal] = 1 medal.

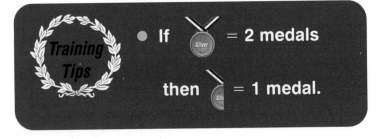